Not Your Average **Oatmeal**

by Abby Regan

To animal foster families that give
and receive love from those that
need a second chance

Not Your Average Oatmeal

by Abby Regan

Bark

Meeeooow!

bark

bark!

Outside of the big city of Chicago, a family who always felt like something was missing began their foster journey to find a furry friend. After facing plenty of disasters as hyper puppies and kittens tore up the furniture around their home, they started to close the foster chapter of their lives.

On their last foster adventure, they met a dog named **Oatmeal.**
But this is not where his story begins...

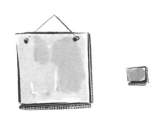

The first home Oats lived in was not a very loving one. He faced injuries in his early years that led him to develop issues when it came to **trusting humans.** When the four-year old pup moved up to Chicago to a foster facility with an injured leg and broken heart, he was picked up by the family to move in until his wounds healed.

On his first day at the family's home, he was surrounded by **new people**, **new smells**, and **new sights** that made him nervous. The first chance he got, Oats took a running start across the backyard and jumped over the tall fence, looking like he could **fly**.

Out into the **unknown town** he went as he crossed **streets**, wrapped around **parks**, and ran through backyards, tracing the scent of other animals, on the hunt for **friends**.

After hours of exploring the town in the 80-degree summer heat, Oats grew hot and tired. He came across a **river** that wrapped around town and jumped in a shallow part to cool off.

Oats walked through the **water**, exploring, and as the stream began to pick up, he could see small **fish** swimming and jumping around his legs. Following the fish, he walked deeper into the stream and went under water to get his fur wet.

Once he grew tired of swimming and was ready to keep exploring, Oats said goodbye to his new fish friends and began his **journey** through town again.

Meanwhile, the family grew beside themselves. It had been a few hours since Oats had broken free from them, and they were upset as this was the first foster animal that got away! They began notifying friends and family to keep their eyes peeled for their **four-legged friend.**

Oats stumbled across the train station where he sat next to a bench on the platform alongside a young family. He **barked** and **barked** as the loud trains stormed by.

The platform was long, so as the trains whizzed by, Oats picked up speed and raced them as far as he could before the platform ended.

After Oats grew tired again, he wandered toward the water tower where he found a freshly dropped vanilla **ice cream cone** and licked it up off the ground. Around the corner from the water tower was a **large open field** where the pup knew his **next adventure** awaited...

Large, white swans were snacking on the tall grass when Oats saw his next opportunity to meet friends. He chased the swans through the field, playing a game of

cat and mouse

until they flew away

from the new mutt in town.

Sad because his new friends flew away, Oats walked to find a new place for friends. Standing on the **swinging bridge** and using his powerful scent to smell the area, Oatmeal grew confused as to who he could trust in the new environment of **animals and humans.**

As it grew dark and the sun started to set, the **family** grew tired of biking and driving around town calling for the pup, and they began to think he was gone for good.

The **family** visited their friend, Police Chief Bailey, of the town police department and asked if he'd had any reports of roaming dogs. Chief Bailey had not, but thankfully the swinging bridge was close to the station, and as Chief Bailey was leaving for the night, **he saw Oats** on the bridge!

Chief Bailey approached the **bridge** slowly, but when Oats heard him with his extraordinary ears, he grew scared again and took off running.

The sun was setting fast, and Oatmeal grew **cold** and **lonely.** Worried about finding a place to sleep that night, he wondered if the family would welcome him back in.

Brrrrr!

Using his strong foxhound **nose** and **senses**, Oats traced his steps back to the house where he first broke free.

And with just one **bark**, the family opened the front door to find their lost friend tired, hungry and cold, but with a big smile on his face to see **familiar faces** again.

Their reunion was **magical**. Oats learned that change might be scary, but he felt something new that he never felt before. Oatmeal gained a **forever home** and family he could trust.

Abby and Oatmeal!

More of Oatmeal's stories and adventures to come...

Printed in the USA
CPSIA information can be obtained
at www.ICGtesting.com
LVHW072145240324
775404LV00012B/132